CORNISH MINING
UNDERGROUND

JABuckley

TOR MARK • REDRUTH

Publisher's note

The text of this book was written in 1989, when three mines were still in operation and the author was working at South Crofty. Since that time all three mines have closed, but the 3000-year-old Cornish tin industry refuses to die. As this edition was going to press early in 2002, there was again some activity at South Crofty. We have decided to leave the 1989 text unaltered, as a record of how things looked to a working miner at that time.

Published by Tor Mark, PO Box 4, Redruth, Cornwall TR16 5YX
First published 1989   Second edition 2002   Reprinted 2004
ISBN 0-85025-396-9

Acknowledgements
The photographs in this book are mostly the work of J C Burrow, supplemented with a few by H W Hughes, and are preserved in the collections of the Royal Institution of Cornwall, to whom the publishers are grateful for permission to reproduce them. The drawing on page 13 is by the author.

Printed in Great Britain by R Booth (The Troutbeck Press), Mabe, Penryn, Cornwall

INTRODUCTION

Few collections of photographs have so captured the atmosphere of a way of life long past as that of J C Burrow. The selection presented here has a unique quality. This highly skilled Victorian photographer caught more than a record of great mines, massive excavations and developing techniques and machinery, valuable though that record is.

Written on the faces of these men long dead is the character of a whole generation of Cornish miners, their grim acceptance of what we would consider appalling working conditions and horrific dangers, in a precarious livelihood. These men never smile or grin at the camera: they have a quiet dignity and strength of character which shines through the mud and sweat on their faces – young boys, men in their full strength of physical maturity and old men who have witnessed every sort of calamity from hunger and poverty to the sudden death of a workmate, friend, neighbour, brother, son. They were men with few illusions about life. No unrealistic hope of sudden wealth influenced them. No retirement cushioned by state pension diverted their view of the future. They were workers. They provided for themselves and their families and would continue to do so until prevented by accident, illness, frail old age or death. When they paused in their work and posed obediently for the mine captain and his visitors, they turned faces to the camera that stated clearly who and what they were.

Burrow did most of his work before the turn of the century, continuing until around 1905, and due to his publication of selected photographs in 'Mongst mines and miners was very well known. Unfortunately the great majority of his glass half-plate negatives were lost during the 1914-18 War, due to the chronic glass shortage, and those that remain have not improved with age. In his book Burrow describes the difficulties of underground photography. Many find it hard enough now, with lightweight, sophisticated equipment, but a century ago it must have been a nightmare. Some mines could transport him and his equipment to the deep levels in a cage, but in many he had to be prepared to climb up and down ladders, rarely firmly secured or uniformly angled. Coping with dirt, moisture and extreme, impenetrable darkness was not easy. Despite the slow laborious business of setting up his equipment, preparing limelight burners and magnesium flares and then posing the miners, Burrow produced pictures of extraordinary quality.

It is not precisely true to say that the world he recorded is now gone, for Cornish miners still spend their working lives in that subterranean world. Many of the conditions have not changed. The descendants of those Victorian and Edwardian miners still toil underground at Geevor, South Crofty and Wheal Jane. Their lives, hopes and aspirations have all changed, as has the gear they use at work, but in many of the faces can still be seen what Burrow captured so long ago.

J E Buckley May 1989

THE LONG ROUTE TO GRASS

A typical scene at East Pool, where the Great Lode and others were mined out for many hundreds of feet. This point is on a main ladderway, as men are coming up from below, then climbing on upward towards the next level, passing two timbermen. Ladders were once the only way to the surface, and in many mines they remained necessary in the deeper levels.

These ladders are of the 'modern' type still used at South Crofty. Squared timbers have holes ready drilled in them to be assembled underground with iron or steel rungs.

A man-engine was a series of platforms carried on a rod which moved up and down with the strokes of an engine at the surface. The miners stepped off at each stationary deck, waited for the rod to descend, then stepped onto the next platform to be raised a further deck. This man engine at Dolcoath was first built in 1854 down to the 248 fathom level when it took 50 minutes to raise a man 'to grass'. After 1876, a new engine brought men from the 314 level in 20 minutes, two fathoms (12ft) at a time.

Accidents were frequent; it was easy to become mesmerised and to fall off, and the rod sometimes broke. This engine was abandoned in 1896, and replaced by gigs and cages.

Gigs for man-riding were originally attached to the whim rope instead of ore-carrying skips. New Cook's Kitchen (later part of South Crofty) still carried men in skips until the late 1930s. This gig at Dolcoath in 1893 could take three miners, but it was very slow and some still preferred to use the ladder alongside. Note the tallow candles hanging from the lower miner's shirtfront. Most mines had a daily issue – at Crofty it was six – and if you could save them by riding in the dark or climbing by the glimmer of your workmate's candle, you could use the saved candles at home.

By the late 1880s, cages were quite common in Cornish mines. Killifreth actually had a 'Yankee' machine – a safety cage that stopped automatically if the rope broke (and it did!).

This is at South Condurrow. Note the open cage – light, and useful for shaft inspection, curved roof for protection from falling objects, elderly lander with 'knocker-line' and the water skip in the parallel skip road, which could supplement the pumps if need be.

SHAFT WORK

Looking down into the very bottom of the Engine Shaft at Cook's Kitchen in 1893. The sump is being drilled deeper by a pneumatic drill, supported by the stretcher bar across the shaft. Several blunted drill steels lie around. Between the ladder and the huge pump valve are timbers up which rock can be hauled in a kibble or bucket.

On the next page you can see the top of this sump, with the kibble being hoisted out. Even the rounded shape of the kibble, and the timber bed, could not prevent both kibbles and timber wearing out very quickly; Cornish mine shafts were rarely vertical (unlike those in collieries) and this caused great expense and inconvenience.

Cook's Kitchen was an ancient mine, known in the seventeenth century as Brea Mine, but by the late nineteenth century it was losing money.

The photograph on the previous page was taken from where, in this picture, the kibble is being tipped into the small half-ton wagon at the 406 fm level. The large compressed air winch is known as a 'larky'. The shaft extends upwards at the far left of the photograph at an angle of about 45°. Up the shaft runs the line of the pump, a skip road (left foreground) up which the kibbles can be hauled, and an air pipe to the pneumatic drill: the fitter seems to be tightening a valve on the airpipe.

Notice how the chain is attached to the kibble in such a way that it tips easily into the wagon – a system still in use today.

Triple clack valve boxes at Carn Brea. Each lift of pumps had these clack valves (so called from the noise they made) to prevent water falling back again. The clacks were seated in leather of buffalo and later of rhino, which was considered best.

Pitmen were responsible for all shaft pump work; it was often very cold and extremely wet work and most miners detested working in the shaft. Few experienced miners would undertake such work if they could avoid it.

Balance bob box. Balance bobs were fixed at regular intervals down a pumping shaft to balance a large part of the weight of the rods which was many tons. The balance bob on the surface could be adjusted very finely by the engineman to minimise the load on the engine and save fuel. The box was filled with old iron and rocks.

This box was at the 236 fm level of the man-engine at Dolcoath, shown on page 5.

GROUND BREAKING

The scene below would have been typical underground before the Great War and in many small mines thereafter. Apart from the St Just district where narrow lodes necessitated one man working alone, the three man group was normal. The senior man (the 'tutworker') held the drill while the two 'boys' (who might be older than the tutworker) struck it. The usual weight of the hammer was five to seven pounds and miners prided themselves on being able to 'beat the borer' from any angle with either hand. The candle is positioned to shine on the drill end which was beaten bright.

These men at East Pool are drilling an 'upper' into the roof at the back of the 'stope' – the area they have been assigned to clear. The diagram illustrates some of the terms used in this book.

The purpose of drilling the hole was to insert an explosive; at this time black powder (gunpowder) was used for preference because it broke a wider area and lifted rock away with less shattering effects upon adjacent rock than dynamite.

On the right is East Pool in 1893, looking down towards the 70 fm level tramroad, which is being reworked. Two miners are drilling the footwall of the lode; they have removed their hard hats for working, as was normal. The figure seated on the rock is the photographer's wife. Notice the great 'stull pieces' which support the jutting part of the hanging wall.

UNDERHAND STOPE

20 FATHOM LEVEL

RAISE

40 FATHOM LEVEL

ENGINE SHAFT

ADIT

WHIM SHAFT

ADIT SHAFT

RIVER

END

BACK STOPE

CHUTES or MILLS

WAGONS

WINSE

SUMP

J.A.Buckley

A magnificent view of a pare (team) of miners working an underhand stope in Carn Brea. The three-man groups were normal; the two pairs are probably each a man short. The ventilation must be good as they are all wearing shirts despite the depth, 285 fathoms. A similar scene is shown on the title page.

Miners hurrying away after lighting three safety fuses. The end of the fuse was cut or pared back to expose dry powder, then lit from a candle. The three-foot fuse gave three minutes burning time in which to get away, after shouting 'Fire!'

Successful shot-hole blasting began in Hungary in 1628 and spread through Germany and England to Cornwall in 1689, where the Cornish took to it faster than in any other area of Britain.

The earliest fuses were quills or lengths of straw and were very dangerous. Safety fuses, invented in Tuckingmill about 1830, saved many lives, but misfires could still be deadly as the powder was picked out of the hole.

South Crofty on 28 February 1910. This reciprocating pneumatic drill, or drifter, is a $3^{1}/_{4}$ in R Stephens & Son 'Climax Imperial'. It was attached to the stretcher bar (with screw jack and chocks of wood to keep it braced) and the drill had a 6 in travel. The water to cool the drill is drawn from a bucket and sprayed onto the point of impact. Such drills were used for the main development at South Crofty from 1880 to 1930.

Note the candle, stuck to the bar by St Agnes clay, sold from the eighteenth century for its tenacity for this purpose.

The boy with the hammer is waiting for the drill to jam, which it often did; he will tap the drill to free it.

Opposite: Two miners stoping the back of a lode, North Crofty 1906. The cover shows a similar scene at Dolcoath. The improvised staging is typical; in the cover picture note the condition of the ladders and the length of old pipe. The mine captain on the left is examining the wall with a candle held close to see the lode structure. The photographer's lighting should not make you forget that the mines were in near total darkness, with only the occasional glimmer of candle.

REMOVAL

An underground steam locomotive had been tried at Levant in 1892 but was defeated by smoke and by the adverse gradient in the 278 fm level: in most mines the level ran downhill to the shaft, but at Levant's 278 fm level it ran uphill. Levant became the only Cornish mine to use ponies underground in the nineteenth century.

Eventually seven ponies were in use. During a strike in 1918, when the pumps were stopped by the strikers, Capt. Ben Nicholas shot the pony on the 350 fm level to save it from drowning.

The wagons are half-ton end tippers, with wheels placed close together in the middle. The photograph on page 2 shows how a similar wagon tipped.

A 'Cousin Jack' chute, so-called because characteristic of Cornish miners, introduced at Dolcoath and taken from there around the world. This early example (Dolcoath, 1893) is of somewhat primitive construction! In many mines, chutes were called 'mills'.

The photograph above shows the function of the chute or mill. The hanging wall is supported by massive stull pieces. The stuff digger above is sorting ore from 'deads', and shovelling the ore into a chute. In the darkness bottom right is a chute with a waiting wagon.

Opposite: Two Cousin Jack chutes in a large stull. Broken ore from the stope came down the chute into the wagons. Hand-tramming was extremely hard work. Note the double-flanged wheels on the wagon: these kept well to the rails, but were murder to push around corners, or where the level was cluttered by rock.

Below is the 375 fm level of Dolcoath, the amazingly wide Main Lode. Dolcoath had been the largest tin producer in Cornwall for fifty years and was still extremely rich, though declining. Few pillars were left as support in the rich ground, hence some of the remarkable 'cut away' photographs such as that of the man-engine.

Notice the long-handled Cornish shovel in use. They were never so common underground as at the surface, because of the narrow, cramped and low workings in many places. Short-handled 'banjo' shovels were commoner, as they are today, but perhaps in the spacious Main Lode the long-handled shovel was no disadvantage.

Notice also the miner's foot behind the shovel, acting as a lever. Digging into an inflexible pile of rocks teaches miners skills different from those of other workers, even in something as basic as shovelling ore.

In 1893 the 412 fm level at Dolcoath was being opened up at great speed, with few pillars left. This area had an ore grade of 10-15%, compared to Crofty's $1^1/2$%. The Great Stull was a wonder of the mining world; mine managers and captains came from all over to view the massive timbers of best pitch pine, each averaging twenty inches square and thirty feet long. Shortly after this photograph was taken a decision was taken to strengthen the stull with new timber. Somehow one of the timbers was allowed to take too much weight and began to move. The hanging wall came in. Eight men were buried and just one was brought out safely, forty hours later.

The untidy level, badly laid track, battered wagons and hectic scene are all typical of miners in too much of a hurry to get the ore out, with safety in second place to greed. After the accident there was much discussion of using masonry instead of timber in such places. Little came of it and they were still talking twenty years later.

TIMBER WORK

Opposite: Two timbermen in a stope, measuring for a stull-piece with a staff of a kind still used at South Crofty – two rods, one fixed, the other sliding, with a wing-nut to clamp it in position. The clamped staff is passed to the mate, who saws planks on the spot, though large timbers are sawn at surface.

Below: This forest of props is a timberman's nightmare. Such random insertion of timber was ruinously expensive, compared to the neat row of timber in a stull, and was the result of problems with hanging walls. Note that even old ladders have been pressed into service!

Blue Hills, St Agnes, the 66 fm level in 1893. St Agnes lodes tended to be very flat; by and large the walls were sound, but when the ore was rich few pillars were left and a large number of stulls or (as here) props were needed. The timberman appears to be beating wooden wedges into the gap at the top of the prop to keep it tight. Timbermen carried, and still carry, wedges to stick in where they think necessary.

Mines tended to have their own bridge designs, and this is typical for East Pool. A wagon is being pushed across, while the intrepid timberman measures for further support timbers in the stull overhead.

Bridges such as this one have been discovered by modern South Crofty miners in the old Pool workings. Very basic engineering principles are used; the verticals of the truss consist of long retaining bolts, probably kept in the stores for this purpose.

This marvellous photograph shows 'the Cathedral', at the 460 ft level in Condurrow Mine, later renamed King Edward Mine. This mine was used by the Camborne School of Mining after it closed commercially in the 1890s and became something of a showplace. Burrow took a number of photographs of students and instructors in this mine, which we have generally avoided using because, although interesting as photographs, they are not a true record of commercial mining, but are posed shots.

Pools such as this are not uncommon and can be quite shallow, or sometimes hundreds of feet deep. The pillar with the hole cut through for access supports the hanging wall: imagine the problems of removing such a large area of rock safely.

Opposite: A vertical lode, narrow by Dolcoath's standards but wide by any other. The next level above runs across the stull on planking. Note the working platform hanging on chains: here it has been partially lowered on one side only.

Most Cornish mines never had a man-engine. Men climbed hundreds of feet at the beginning and end of every core shift, often in heat and wet, and while exhausted. Climbing a relatively flat ladderway like this is not easy and can be more tiring than climbing a vertical ladder. To save money on candles, miners sometimes lit just one for every three or four men climbing.

A group of East Pool miners at croust time, or 'morzel time' as it is called in the St Just area. This was, and is, usually about two-thirds of the way through the core, at around 11am on the 'forenoon core'. Most of the men are eating pasties wrapped in a cloth; a traditional water barrel can be seen in the left foreground, and one of the men on the left is drinking from another. Some have clay pipes.

The men at the back and the left are on croust seats, the rest have been gathered for the photograph. Miners never sit on the floor for croust. A new work area requires a new croust seat as its first priority.

We have included this picture despite the stain on the glass negative, because it uniquely shows the enormous width of Dolcoath's Main Lode, the greatest, richest, widest and most famous tin lode in Cornwall, or perhaps in the world. The miners are standing on a 'horse' of ground between two branches of Main Lode; notice the huge timber supports bottom right. The lode itself runs at about 45° at this point (440 fm) and despite the collapse of Great Stull ten years earlier, there is still no general support for the roof.

Notice how the candles are spread out, on men's hats and at working places. The brief illumination for Burrow's photograph would have been the only time these men saw the great cave they had created.